Fruits and Seeds

Kenna Bourke, Ros
and Gill Matt

Contents

OXFORD
UNIVERSITY PRESS

The King of Fruits

Kenna Bourke

Jack stared at the mirror. The face in the mirror stared back.

"My teeth aren't straight," thought Jack. "My eyes are too small, and my ears stick out."

"Everyone says I'm ugly. They're right, I am ugly," he said to the mirror.

"When I grow up, no one will want me for a friend. I'll go on getting uglier and uglier and uglier." Jack threw himself on to his bed and buried his face in the pillow.

Three doors away Mimosa Mudface was also looking in the mirror. She was about to go to a birthday party.

"Oh, you are so beautiful," said her mother, beaming with pride.

"Yes, I am," thought Mimosa. "I have a perfect face, big brown eyes, glossy hair, and I'm wearing the loveliest dress you could ever wish to have."

Then Mr Mudface poked his head round the bedroom door. "Oh, what a pretty princess my daughter is!" he gasped.

Mimosa took one last long look in the mirror and blew a kiss to herself.

On Monday morning, Jack and Mimosa were in Miss Lim's class, as usual. It was Science. Mimosa hated Science. Jack loved it.

"Plant seeds are spread in different ways," said Miss Lim. "Who can tell me one of the ways they're spread?"

Mimosa gulped.

"Are you OK?" asked Jack, kindly. "Do you want any help?"

"Ewww! Go away, you ugly, ugly boy!" hissed Mimosa.

Twenty heads turned to look at Jack. There was snorting and smirking and giggling. Harry Chan was laughing so much that he fell off his chair on to the floor. "Ugly Jack, Ugly Jack!" chanted Mimosa and her friends.

At break time, Jack went into the playground and sat alone under a tree. "I'm ugly," he thought. "Ugly equals nasty, and nasty equals no friends. That's all there is to it. It's simple maths."

Just then, a monkey swung down from a high branch.

"Psst!" said the monkey. "Hey, you! Over here!"

Jack had never spoken to a monkey before. Even so he climbed up the tree and sat on a branch.

"Feeling ugly?" asked the monkey.

"Well, yes…" said Jack rather shyly. "Everyone says I'm ugly, so I must be."

"What nonsense," laughed the monkey, picking a ripe banana. "Let me ask you a question. Are you a nice person?"

"Well, I suppose so, yes, but that's no good because I'm ugly," said Jack.

"Don't you know anything?" asked the monkey, impatiently.

"What do you mean?"
stammered Jack. The monkey grinned
and took a large bite of his banana.
"The thing is, Jack, ugliness doesn't exist. Not
really. It's something that you imagine is in other
people's minds. Here, take one of these and you can
find out for yourself."

The monkey passed him a tiny packet made of
leaves. The label on it said, "*Fast-growing **durian***".

"What's this? What do I do with it? Will it stop me
being ugly?" Jack shouted, but the monkey had
scampered off into the trees.

The bell for the end of break brought Jack back to reality. He scrambled down from the tree and ran back to the classroom, stuffing the precious package into his pocket.

That evening, when everyone had gone to bed, Jack decided to take a closer look at the monkey's curious present. He opened it carefully and found just one seed inside.

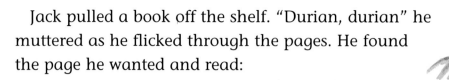

Jack pulled a book off the shelf. "Durian, durian" he muttered as he flicked through the pages. He found the page he wanted and read:

*"The durian is a fruit-bearing tree
of south-eastern Asia."*

Reading on, Jack's heart sank as he discovered that the durian took up to ten years to grow and produce fruit. He looked in the mirror again. "In ten years' time, I'll be nearly eighteen, and ten times as ugly as I am now," he thought sadly. But then he remembered the writing on the label: *"Fast-growing durian"*, so perhaps there was hope, after all.

As soon as it was morning, Jack rushed outside into the bright sunlight. He chose a spot of land that he could see from his bedroom window, and began to dig.

Very carefully, Jack took the seed from the package and placed it in the hole. He covered it gently with earth and gave it a little water. "Please grow," he whispered, "and please make me less ugly."

Mimosa Mudface was smirking in the most unpleasant way when Jack arrived at school that morning. She'd seen Jack planting the seed. Worse still, she'd told the whole class!

> *"Ugly Jack … planted a seed …*
> *What did he grow?*
> *Just a weed!"*

The other children chanted a silly song to tease Jack.
Jack felt really miserable. He wasn't just ugly but stupid, too. After all, no one sensible would listen to a monkey, would they?

The minute school was over, Jack ran home as fast as he could. He threw his school bag on to the floor and stared miserably out of his window into the clear blue sky. Or at least he tried to.

Where once there had been an empty patch of grassland, there now stood the most enormous tree. Jack threw open the window and was almost knocked out by the strongest smell that had ever hit his nostrils: a strange mixture of rotten onions, rotten eggs, blocked drains, old cheese and dustbins. Jack held his nose and peered at the tree. It was covered in hedgehogs! Huge, green, spiky hedgehogs!

Jack rushed outside. As he got closer to the tree, he saw that the hedgehogs were actually growing on it. Then he remembered something he had once seen at the airport. It was a sign that looked like this:

Jack's mum and dad had told him the durian was such a smelly fruit that some hotels and airports would not allow people to carry it. But then he remembered he had been told a very important thing: this ugly, smelly, prickly old fruit was also really delicious!

Jack raced back to find his book. Yes, this really was the durian! *"The King of fruits,"* it said, *"a much-prized **delicacy"**.*

Jack went back to the tree and stared at it. He couldn't believe that it was his. Then he heard footsteps and chanting behind him. It was Mimosa and seven of her friends. But the chanting soon stopped when they saw the tree. They ran towards it in disbelief. To Jack's amazement, a durian fruit dropped to the ground, missing Mimosa by a whisker.

Jack looked up and saw the monkey on the branch. He was grinning. "Not a bad shot, was it, Jack?" he giggled. Jack winked.

"Look at the ugly fruit that ugly Jack has grown!" squawked Mimosa.

The monkey swung down from the tree like an acrobat and started to eat the fallen durian. "Come on, Jack," he said, "It's your fruit. You grew it, you try it!"

Jack tucked in. It was the most delicious thing he'd ever tasted! It was like custard and honey and candy floss and tropical fruit juice all rolled into one. By now all the children were gobbling the fruit up. Even Mimosa had stopped sneering and was covered in durian juice.

"This is wonderful, Jack," she said, "You're quite clever really, aren't you? I think you must be a magician." It was odd. She was actually being nice.

"But I'm still ugly," Jack whispered to the monkey.

"Oh, dear," groaned the monkey. "You don't understand, do you? Listen carefully while I explain it to you."

He leant over and whispered in Jack's ear, "This is an ugly fruit. It even smells terrible. But it's delicious and everyone loves it."

"Yes, but, so what?" said Jack anxiously.

"It's what you're like on the inside that matters, silly!" replied the monkey.

Jack looked at the monkey, took a very large bite of durian, and smiled.

15

Grow your own Seeds and Beans

Gill Matthews

Have you ever tried growing your own food?
Follow these instructions and you'll soon
have the **ingredients** for a delicious salad.

NASTURTIUMS

You can plant these indoors in Spring, or outdoors in Summer.

You will need:
- container (20 cm wide)
- small stones
- **compost**
- 6 nasturtium seeds

What you do:

1 Fill the container about
one-third full of the small
stones.

small stones
⅓

2 Spread compost on top of
the stones.

compost

GROWING TIP Look out for caterpillars, they will eat the plants faster than you!

16

3 Plant 6 nasturtium seeds 1.5 cm deep in the compost.

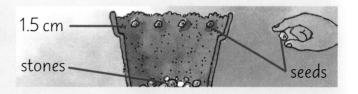

1.5 cm

stones

seeds

4 Water the compost well and place the container in a warm, sunny place.

water

5 After 10–12 days the seeds will **sprout**.

6 Plant the seedlings in the garden when they are 8 cm high. Keep them watered.

seedlings

water

7 In about 3 months the nasturtiums will flower and will be ready to **harvest**.

8 With help from an adult, cut the flowers and leaves as you need them.

flowers

leaves

SERVING SUGGESTION Both the leaves and flowers can be eaten raw in salads.

MUNG BEANS

You can grow these indoors at any time of year.

You will need:
- one packet of mung beans
- bowl
- sieve
- damp cottonwool
- flat tray
- cling film
- newspaper

What you do:

1 Tip the beans into a bowl. Cover them in cold water and soak overnight.

2 Pour the beans into a sieve and rinse them well under cold water.

3 Place the damp cottonwool in the bottom of the tray.

4 Spread the mung beans evenly over the cottonwool.

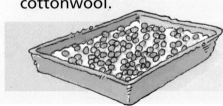

Keep the beans moist but not too wet, otherwise they will go **mouldy**.

5 Cover the tray with cling film.

6 Place newspaper over the cling film to keep out the light.

7 Check the tray every day to make sure that the cottonwool is moist. If it is dry, sprinkle it with water.

8 Once the beans begin to sprout, take off the newspaper and cling film.

9 After 6–9 days the mung beans will be ready to harvest. The bean sprouts should be 25–38 mm long, about as long as your little finger.

10 Take out any beans that have not sprouted. Rinse the sprouts well under cold water.

Mung beans can be eaten raw in a salad. They can also be cooked for 2 minutes in boiling water or used in a **stir fry**.

CRESS SHAPES

You can grow these indoors at any time of year.

You will need:
- packet of cress seeds
- flat tray
- 10 sheets of kitchen towel
- biscuit cutters
- plastic carrier bag

What you do:

1 Place the sheets of kitchen towel in the tray. Sprinkle cold water over the kitchen towel so that it is damp.

water

kitchen towel

2 Put the biscuit cutters on the kitchen towel and spread the cress seeds evenly inside them.

3 Remove the biscuit cutters, taking care not to disturb the seeds.

seeds

cutters

4 Place the tray inside the carrier bag and put it in a dark place.

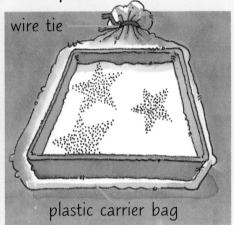

wire tie

plastic carrier bag

5 After two or three days the seeds will sprout. Take the tray out of the bag and put it in on a warm window sill.

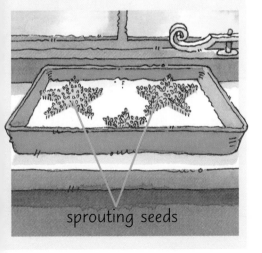

sprouting seeds

GROWING TIP

Keep the kitchen towel moist otherwise the cress will not grow.

6 In 10–12 days the cress will be ready to harvest.

7 With help from an adult, cut off the cress with scissors as you need it.

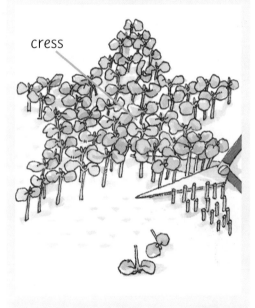

cress

SERVING SUGGESTION

Egg sandwiches taste great with cress. You can also scatter cress on a salad.

GROWING CHART

The chart shows you when to plant, how long it takes for the seeds to sprout, and when best to harvest. It also shows you what you can do with the plants once they have been harvested.

	NASTURTIUM	MUNG BEANS	CRESS
Plant	Spring	any time	any time
Sprout	10–12 days	3–4 days	2–3 days
Harvest	3 months	6–9 days	10–12 days
Use	salad	salad cooked vegetable stir fry	salad sandwiches

The Wonderful Tree

A SOUTH AMERICAN MYTH

Rosalind Kerven

Long, long ago when the world was new, an animal
got lost in the great, spreading forest. This animal was
the **agouti**. He ran here and there, under the bushes
and creepers, ears pricked, whiskers twitching,
desperately trying to find his way home.

Suddenly he noticed a strange and delicious
smell. Agouti had no idea what it was.
But if you had smelt it, it would have
reminded you of chocolate and sweetcorn
in chilli-sauce, mixed up with many
kinds of juicy tropical fruits.

Whatever could it be?

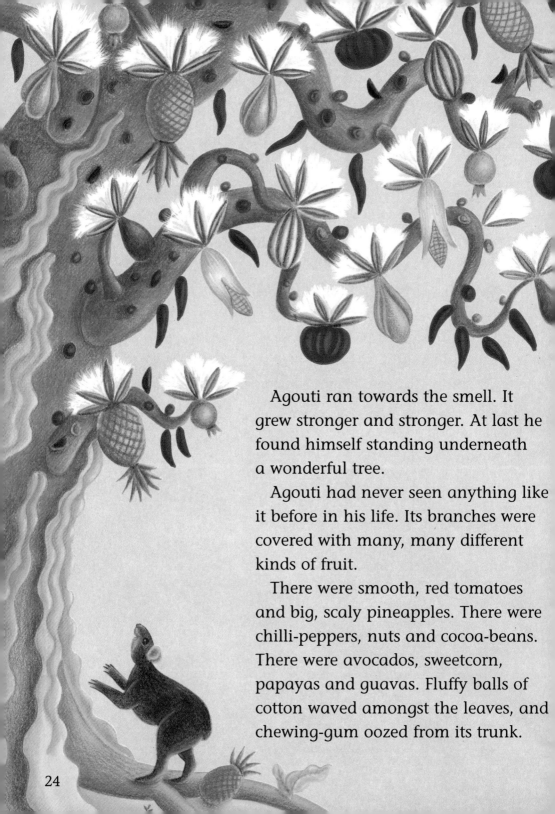

Agouti ran towards the smell. It grew stronger and stronger. At last he found himself standing underneath a wonderful tree.

Agouti had never seen anything like it before in his life. Its branches were covered with many, many different kinds of fruit.

There were smooth, red tomatoes and big, scaly pineapples. There were chilli-peppers, nuts and cocoa-beans. There were avocados, sweetcorn, papayas and guavas. Fluffy balls of cotton waved amongst the leaves, and chewing-gum oozed from its trunk.

Agouti's mouth watered. He licked his lips. Then he ran up the trunk and along the branches. He couldn't wait to taste all the wonderful fruit!

Soon he was busy gobbling up bits of this and bits of that. He coughed over the chilli-peppers and pieces of yellow sweetcorn and red tomato pips got stuck all over his fur.

Agouti felt so full, he thought he would burst! When he really couldn't eat any more, he made himself a nest amongst the cotton buds, and fell fast asleep.

Hours later he woke up and ran down the tree trunk. He found the track he had made through the forest, and followed it back until he reached his burrow.

His brother was waiting for him there. "Wherever have you been all this time?" he cried.

"Oh… you know, just here and there," said Agouti.

"What's all that mess in your fur?" asked his brother.

"Oh… just this and that," said Agouti.

He had decided that the wonderful tree would be his own special secret. He didn't want anyone else to taste its delicious fruit – not even his own brother.

Time passed. When no one else was looking, Agouti often sneaked back to the wonderful tree. There he would feast on its many different fruits, chew on its oozing gum, and doze amongst the soft cotton.

He got fatter and fatter. Soon all the other forest animals began to talk about him. They asked questions about where he kept sneaking off to, and why.

For a long time, Agouti refused to tell anyone his secret. But one day he couldn't stop himself from boasting, and told his brother all about the wonderful tree.

"Ohoh!" said his brother, "this is very interesting. I'd like to see this tree for myself. Show me!"

Agouti didn't want to. But his brother kept pestering him, until at last he gave in.

Agouti led his brother down the long, twisting secret forest tracks that led to the wonderful tree.

His brother's eyes gleamed when he saw it.

"Let's cut it down," he said.

"Why?" said Agouti.

"Then we can hide it properly," said his brother, "and make sure no one else ever finds it."

So Agouti and his brother began to nibble and gnaw
at the roots and trunk of the wonderful tree.

The tree creaked and bent. They nibbled and gnawed
some more...

Suddenly there was a great clap of thunder!

The tree's trunk burst wide open. Water came gushing out of it.
It spread away and out across the earth, on and on, in a great
flood. It didn't stop until the forest
had become a huge, blue sea.

Then the whole tree toppled
over, falling heavily to the
ground with a loud CRASH!

A wind blew up. It turned into a gale, and then a hurricane.

The wind pulled at the fruits and tore them from the wonderful tree's branches. It whirled them into the air. Soon the sky was full of pineapples and papaya, spicy chillis and sticky gum, golden corn and green avocados. They spun round and round in a great cloud, up and over the forest, out into the big, wide world.

Agouti and his brother stared after them in dismay. All the fruits had gone!

There were some farmers who lived outside the forest. They found the wind-blown fruits, picked them up, and tasted them. The fruits were delicious. They decided to plant the pips and fruit-stones to see if they would grow. Before long the farmers had fields full of the delicious fruits.

So that is how farmers grew their first crops. But nothing like the wonderful tree has ever been seen again.

Glossary

agouti   An agouti is a small furry animal, like a guinea pig, that lives in South America.

compost   Compost is a dry crumbly mixture used as plant food. It is made from old plant material such as rotting leaves, stalks and vegetable peelings.

delicacy   A delicacy is a particularly delicious food.

durian   The durian tree is a large tree that grows in south-east Asia. It has spiny fruit filled with a creamy pulp that smells bad but tastes delicious.

harvest   To harvest means to gather in the crops. The crops are gathered at harvest time.

ingredients   A mixture is made up of ingredients. A recipe includes a list of the ingredients you will need – to make a cake, for example.

mouldy   If food or a plant is left in a damp place, it may go mouldy. Mould is a furry growth that appears on the surface because the food or plant has gone bad.

sprout   A sprout is a small shoot that appears when a seed or plant begins to grow.

stir fry   A stir fry is a cooked food mixture containing mainly vegetables. They are stirred and tossed while they are fried quickly.